Discover
PEOPLE AND
PLACES

Reading
CHALLENGE®

Visit us at www.readingchallenge.com

Contents

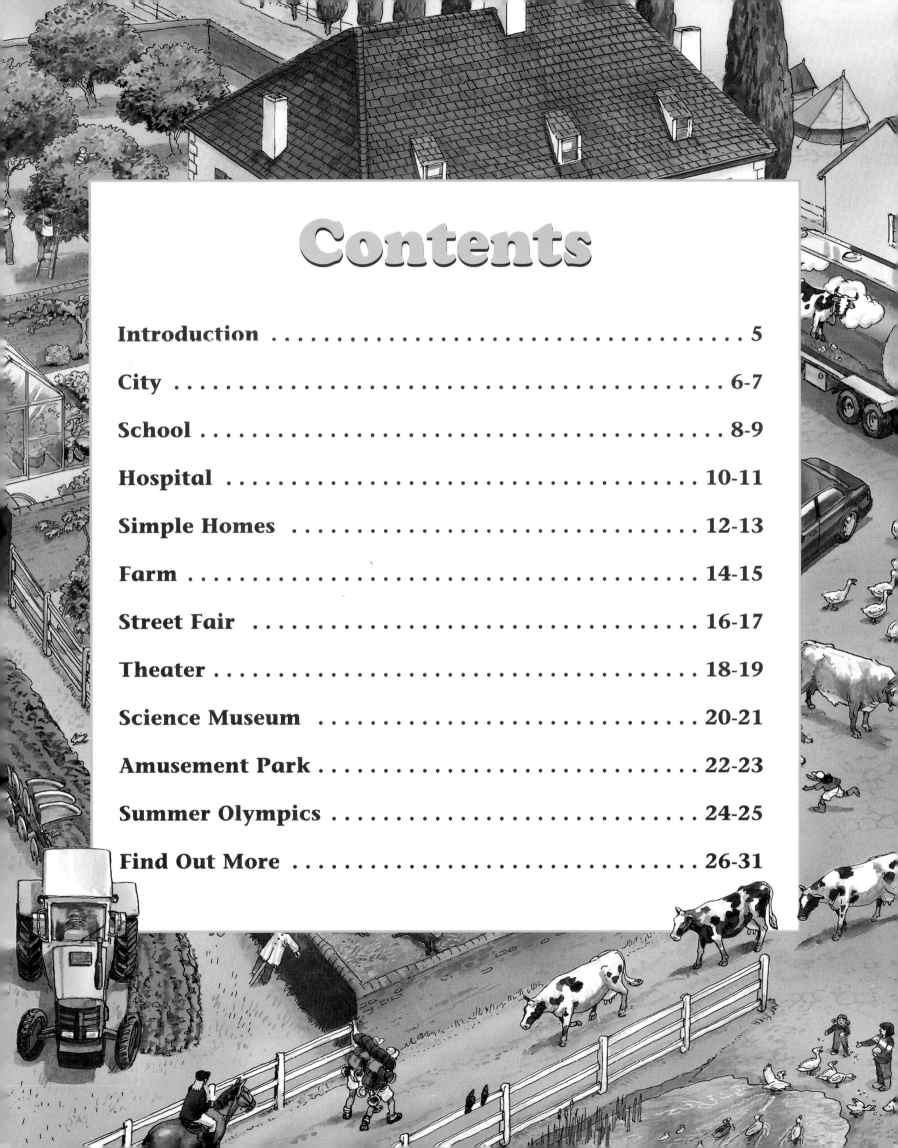

Introduction

In our world there are many talented and hard-working people who accomplish amazing things.

PEOPLE AND PLACES will take you on a journey into the lives of interesting people. You will visit exciting locations where they work, live, and play. Wonderful illustrations and fun search and find activities will help you learn about what it is like to run a farm, or sell toys at a street fair.

In addition, a **Find Out More** section in the back is packed with facts, trivia, and websites so you can learn more about each subject illustrated in the book.

So get your camera and get ready to
Read, Search & Find™ as you
Discover
PEOPLE AND PLACES!

City

A city is a very busy place. Some people work in offices. Others go to the movies or visit museums. Children play in the park. Taxis, buses, and trolleys take people where they want to go. Many people also walk to get around. There are lots of things to see and do in a city.

Search & Find

- [ ] **Beds (3)**
- [ ] **Benches (2)**
- [ ] **Frisbee**
- [ ] **Guitar player**
- [ ] **Motorcycles (3)**
- [ ] **People riding bicycles (4)**
- [ ] **People walking dogs (4)**
- [ ] **Skateboarder**

Restaurant
Cities have many different kinds of restaurants.

Art museum
People visit art museums to look at paintings and other works of art.

Taxi
People pay taxi drivers to take them places.

Swings
There are lots of parks in a city. Most of them have a swing set and slide to play on.

Shopping
A city has many different stores. Some people visit the city just to go shopping!

Trolley
This trolley runs on electricity. It rides on rails, like a train.

Find Out More
on page 26

7

School

Children go to school to learn about many different things. In one classroom, they might learn about reading and math. In another classroom, they might learn about art or music. There are many interesting things happening in this school. These children look like they are having a lot of fun.

Search & Find

- [ ] Cactus
- [ ] Computers (2)
- [ ] Garbage cans (2)
- [ ] Globe
- [ ] Lost shoes (3)
- [ ] Pair of boots
- [ ] Trophy
- [ ] Toy elephant

Kitchen
Some children learn how to cook in school.

Computer time
These children are using the computer to learn.

Cleaning up
Everyone takes turns and helps clean up in class.

Gym class
The gym is a place to excercise and have fun playing games.

Class pet
Hamsters and gerbils are popular class pets. Children learn how to take care of them.

Front office
This girl is starting her first day at school. The woman at the desk will help her find her classroom.

Library
Children go to the library to look for books. This girl is reading her book.

Blackboard
Teachers ask the children to solve problems at the blackboard.

Find Out More
on page 27

9

Hospital

A hospital is where people who are sick or hurt go to get help. Doctors and nurses help them get better. In some hospital rooms, doctors operate on very sick people. Many rooms in the hospital are where patients stay until they are feeling well enough to go home. Not everyone in a hospital is sick. Babies are born there, too.

Search & Find

- [ ] Aliens (4)
- [ ] Clown
- [ ] Doctor washing his hands
- [ ] Pillow fight
- [ ] Snake
- [ ] Vacuum cleaner
- [ ] Wheelchairs (9)

Waiting room

Family and friends stay here while they wait to hear about a patient.

Operating room

Doctors might need to do an operation to help a sick or injured person get better.

X-ray machine

An X-ray machine takes pictures of the inside of a person's body.

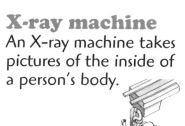

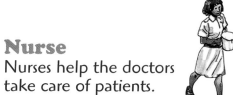

Nurse

Nurses help the doctors take care of patients.

Doctor

Doctors try to help sick people get well again.

Emergency room

Some people need a doctor's help right away. They are taken right to the emergency room.

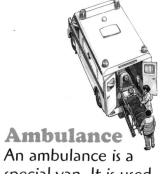

Ambulance

An ambulance is a special van. It is used to rush sick or injured people to a hospital.

Find Out More
on page 27

11

Simple Homes

In some parts of the world, people live in very simple homes. Some people live in mud huts. Others may live in tree houses or sleep in tents. There are places where an entire village is built on stilts over the water!

Search & Find

- ☐ Camels (4)
- ☐ Dogs (4)
- ☐ Fires (3)
- ☐ Goat
- ☐ Hammock
- ☐ Pig
- ☐ Pole climbers (2)
- ☐ Spear

Tent
Some people live in deserts and travel from place to place. They sleep in tents at night.

House on stilts
Some people live on lakes or in flood areas. They build their homes over the water.

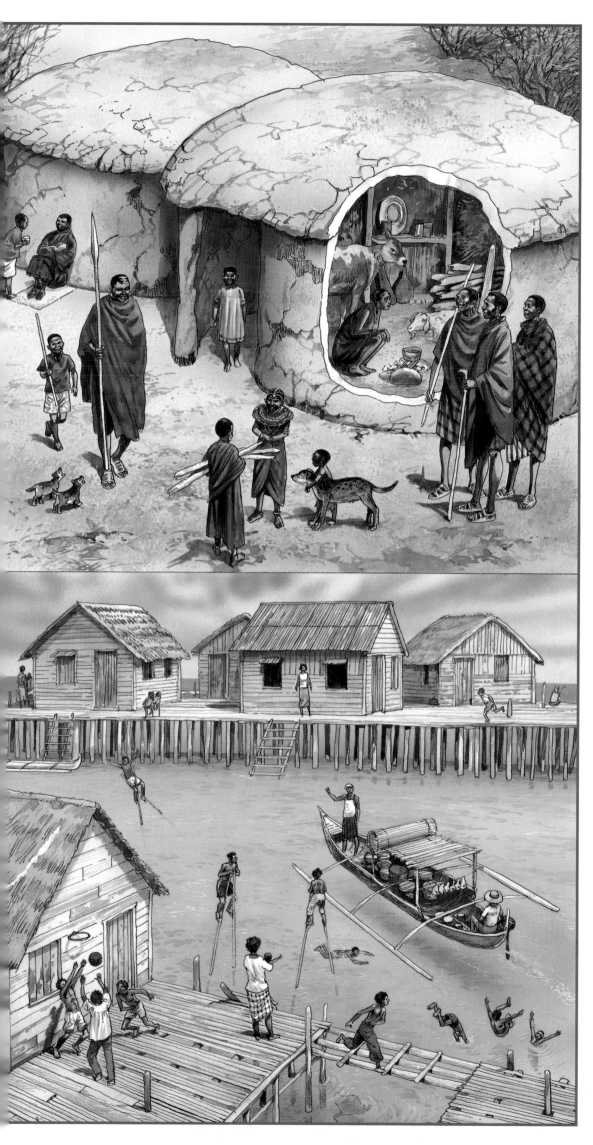

Walking on stilts

This person is using stilts to walk above the water.

Cutting wood

This man is using a large, heavy knife to cut wood for his tree house.

Cooking

Many people cook their food over fires.

Tree house

In rain forests, some families live in tree houses. This boy is climbing a pole ladder to get to his house.

Find Out More on page 28

Farm

Many people help do the work on a farm. The farmer milks the cows and feeds the pigs. A farmhand takes care of the horses and cleans the stables. Other helpers pick apples and feed the geese. The wheat in one field is harvested, while a plow gets another field ready to be planted. There are many things to do on a farm!

Search & Find

- [ ] **Backpackers (2)**
- [ ] **Bicycles (2)**
- [ ] **Blackbirds (10)**
- [ ] **Horses (4)**
- [ ] **Ladder**
- [ ] **Rabbits (6)**
- [ ] **Sheep getting away**

Feeding geese
This farmer raises geese for meat and feathers. Geese are larger than ducks, but smaller than swans.

Sheep
A farmer shaves the wool off the sheep. The wool can be used to make clothes.

Vegetable garden
There is a vegetable garden next to the house. The family eats the vegetables from the garden.

Farmhand
The farmhand helps do the work around the farm.

Plow

A plow breaks up the soil so the farmer can plant seeds. A plow also gets rid of weeds.

Greenhouse

The greenhouse gives shelter for young plants. It is made of glass and is very warm inside.

Stables

Horses eat and sleep in stables. The stables are inside the barn.

Combine

A combine (KAHM-byne) is a machine used to harvest wheat. In the old days, it was pulled by horses.

Milking the cows

Cows give us milk. We make things like cheese and yogurt from their milk.

Find Out More
on page 28

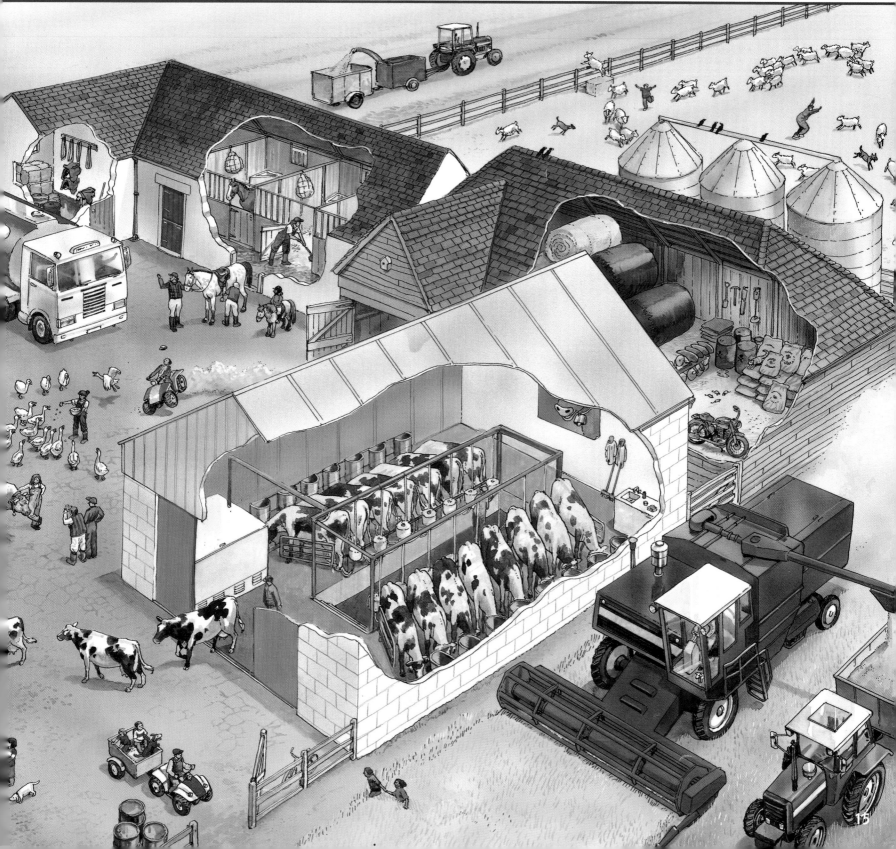

15

Street Fair

There is a lot to do and see at a street fair. At one stall, an artist is drawing pictures of people. At another stall, someone is selling food. Old toys, T-shirts, vegetables, flowers, and many other things are for sale. This is a fun place to be!

Search & Find

- ☐ Banana peel
- ☐ Bicycle
- ☐ Clock
- ☐ Dog balloons (4)
- ☐ Remote-control car
- ☐ Strollers (2)

16

Barbecue chicken

People sell many different kinds of food. Barbecue (BAR-buh-kyoo) chicken is often a favorite!

Artist

This artist draws very quickly! In a short time, the picture of the girl will be finished.

Balloon seller

Balloons come in all shapes and sizes. Some even look like dogs.

Bookseller

You can usually find all kinds of books at street fairs.

Toys

There are lots of things to buy at this steet fair— even stuffed animals.

Candy stand

Children like to visit the candy stand at the street fair.

Flower stand

This person sells flowers that she grew in her garden. Her stand is very colorful.

Find Out More on page 29

17

Theater

At a theater, actors perform plays. Plays are stories that people act out. Musicians sit in front of the stage. Some people help with the costumes and scenery (SEE-nuh-ree). Plays can be very exciting. Hurry! This one has already begun.

Search & Find

- ☐ Crown
- ☐ Dog
- ☐ Paper airplane
- ☐ Piano
- ☐ Pitch fork
- ☐ Stars (2)
- ☐ Tin man
- ☐ Wizard

Find Out More
on page 29

Buying tickets

You need to buy a ticket if you want to see the show.

Usher

An usher helps people find their seats.

Actors

These actors are getting ready to go out on stage.

Stagehand

Stagehands help put on a play. Some might move scenery or help the actors. They make sure that everything is in the right place during the play.

Stage manager

The stage manager is in charge of everything that happens on the stage during the play.

Musician

This man is playing the piano. A large group of musicians playing together is called an orchestra (OR-kuh-struh).

Science Museum

Exploring this museum is a fun way to learn about science. Some machines make waves or whirlpools. Others make lightning or X rays. Special mirrors make people look bigger or smaller. Children can play with the machines and even check their own heartbeats.

Search & Find

- [ ] American flag
- [ ] Arrow
- [ ] Flying reptile
- [ ] Man taking pictures
- [ ] Skull and crossbones
- [ ] Star
- [ ] Toy boats (2)
- [ ] Wave machine

X ray
An X ray shows what bones look like inside the body.

Planet with rings
Some planets have rings around them. Saturn has rings made of pieces of ice.

Giant piano
These children can play a song by jumping from key to key!

Whirlpool controls
This boy controls the speed and strength of the whirlpool.

Lightning
This machine shows how lightning works.

Magnet
This magnet is strong enough to pull a dog into the air!

Find Out More on page 30

Amusement Park

Amusement parks are a lot of fun! This is a "Wild West" park. It has pony rides and a rodeo. Actors dressed as cowboys and Native Americans put on shows. They act out scenes from the Old West. There are also many tasty treats to eat. An amusement park is a great place to spend the day with family and friends.

Search & Find

- [ ] Cactuses (9)
- [ ] Escaping balloon
- [ ] Flags (17)
- [ ] Lassos (2)
- [ ] Loudspeakers (2)
- [ ] Photographer
- [ ] Satellite dish
- [ ] Strollers (3)

Cowboy
This cowboy is trying to catch a bull with his rope. The rope is called a lasso (LA-so).

Prairie dogs
Most parks serve hot dogs. Here they are called prairie dogs.

Clown
Clowns are a familiar sight at amusement parks. This one is selling balloons.

Find Out More
on page 30

Train ride

This train goes around the park, picking people up and dropping them off at the station.

Pony rides

Ponies are small horses. They are the perfect size for children to ride.

Rodeo

At the rodeo, cowboys ride bulls for as long as they can without falling off. The bulls are strong, but so are the riders!

Cactus

Cactus plants grow in the dry deserts of the West. They can grow tall without much water.

Rides

There are many fun rides at the amusement park.

Summer Olympics

The Summer Olympic Games take place every four years. The best athletes from around the world come to compete. In this stadium, track-and-field events are taking place. Winning a medal at the Olympics is a great honor.

Search & Find

- [ ] **Chair tipping over**
- [ ] **Falling runner**
- [ ] **Man on stretcher**
- [ ] **Olympic rings (7)**
- [ ] **Pail and shovel**
- [ ] **Pole vaulter**
- [ ] **Rabbit**
- [ ] **TV cameras (9)**

Judges
Judges score each athlete's performance. They decide who wins some of the events.

Olympic flame
The Olympic torch is used to light a flame during the opening ceremony. This flame stays lit throughout the Games.

Long jump
In this event, an athlete jumps as far as he or she can.

High jump
In this event, athletes must jump over a pole without knocking it down.

Sprinter
Sprinters run as fast as they can for a short distance.

Medals podium
When winning athletes receive their medal, they stand on a podium so everyone can see them.

Find Out More on page31

Find Out More

City

New York City is the largest city in the United States. More than eight million people live there.

Visitors to a city often stay in a hotel. This man is asleep in his hotel room. Hotel workers keep the rooms clean.

Every state in the United States has its own capital city. Washington, D.C., is the capital city of the whole United States.

About one half of all the people in the world live in cities.

Most people who live in a city live in an apartment building.

Many companies have offices in a city. These people are busy working on computers.

Chicago, Illinois, is called the Windy City. Strong winds blow off nearby Lake Michigan.

Learn more at:

www.city-data.com/

http://factfinder.census.gov/home/en/kids/kids.html

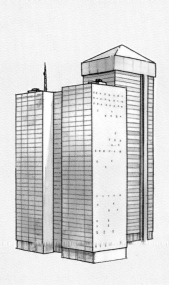

School

There are different kinds of schools. Some are public. Others are private or religious. Some children are schooled at home.

Most public schools have computers for children to use.

In school, children learn to play and share with others. School is a good place to make new friends.

There are about four million teachers in the United States.

All children learn reading, writing, and math in school.

Learn more at:

www.funschool.com/

http://school.discovery.com/

www.historyforkids.org/

Hospital

There are different areas, called wards, in a hospital. The place where babies are born is called the maternity (muh-TUR-nuh-tee) ward.

A doctor who takes care of children is called a pediatrician (PEE-dee-uh-TRIH-shun).

This patient is doing special exercises. Soon her muscles will become strong again.

A doctor who operates on a patient is called a surgeon (SIR-jin).

Some hospitals care for people with all kinds of sickness or injuries. Other hospitals treat only people who have a particular sickness.

Hospitals were started by the ancient Romans over 2,000 years ago.

Learn more at:

http://kidshealth.org/kid/

www.brainpop.com/health/seeall/

Simple Homes

Some people who live in deserts still travel by camel. Today, many use cars or trucks.

Many people who live in rain forests hunt for their food. They also make medicine from the plants in the rain forest.

Huts made out of mud help people stay cool during the day and warm at night. Sometimes animals stay in the hut, too.

Children who live in houses on the water spend a lot of time swimming!

These boys have to be careful. Their ball might fall in the water!

Learn more at:

http://habitatforhumanity.org.uk/html/worldwide_houses.html

Farm

Agriculture (AG-grih-KUL-chur) is the science of raising crops and farm animals.

There are more than two million farms in the United States.

A milk truck takes milk from the farm to a dairy that will put it in cartons. This special truck keeps the milk fresh and cold.

It takes about ten pounds of milk to make one pound of cheese.

On the farm, pigs live in a pen called a sty. The sty is very muddy but the pigs love it!

Corn is grown on every continent except Antarctica.

Wheat is what farmers all over the world grow the most.

Learn more at:

www.agclassroom.org

www.fsa.usda.gov/ca/agforkids.htm

www.usda.gov/news/usdakids

Street Fair

A person who sells things at a fair is called a vendor (VEN-dur).

This boy is drinking some fresh orange juice.

There are different types of street fairs. Some offer a little bit of everything. Others offer only one kind of thing, such as art or food.

The first street art fair was held in Ann Arbor, Michigan, in 1960. More than 500,000 people visit the fair every year.

Many handmade things are sold at a street fair.

You can find almost anything at a street fair—even music!

Learn more at:

www.artfair.org

www.NihonmachiStreetFair.org

Theater

This actor appears through a trapdoor in the stage. Special effects are used to create smoke.

The most famous writer of plays is William Shakespeare (SHAKE-speer). He lived in England, during the late 1500s and early 1600s.

The oldest plays were written in ancient Greece more than 2,300 years ago.

Broadway is an area in New York City that has many theaters. It is known as the Great White Way because of all the bright lights outside the theaters.

The conductor directs the orchestra. The musicians watch the conductor to make sure they play at the right time.

Learn more at:

www.americantheaterweb.com

www.broadwaytheater.com

Science Museum

Art, natural history, and science are only three of the many different types of museums.

The American Museum of Natural History in New York City is famous for its huge collection of dinosaur skeletons.

The curved mirrors make people look very strange!

The Smithsonian Institution in Washington, D.C., has 16 museums and a zoo.

This girl is filming her own video using a real TV camera.

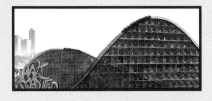

At a museum in Cincinnati, there is a pile of garbage that is 25-feet tall. That is how much trash an American family of four people throws away each month.

Learn more at:

www.exploratorium.edu

www.smithsonianeducation.org/students/

www.fieldmuseum.org

Amusement Park

The roller coaster is one of the most popular rides at an amusement park.

The largest drive-through wild-animal park outside of Africa is in New Jersey.

Walt Disney World has four different theme parks plus two water parks.

Games, rides, music, and shows can all be found at an amusement park.

Lake Compounce in Bristol, Connecticut, is the oldest amusement park in the United States. It opened in 1846.

A ride in an old stagecoach is fun.

Learn more at:

www.lakecompounce.com

www.themeparksonline.org

Summer Olympics

The five rings in the Olympics symbol represent the five continents whose countries take part in the Olympic Games.

The winner of each event receives a gold medal. A silver medal goes to the second-place winner. A bronze medal goes to the athlete who comes in third.

The first Olympic flame was lit in 1928 at the Olympic Games in Amsterdam.

The first modern Olympic Games took place in Athens, Greece, in 1894. The athletes competed in 43 events. In 2004, the Summer Olympics returned to Athens. That time, there were 301 events!

Doctors are always nearby at the events. Here, the doctor examines an athlete who has hurt her ankle.

The Olympic Games include both individual and team sports. From time to time, new sports are added and old ones are dropped.

Learn more at:

www.athens2004.com

www.olympic.org